UPS AND DOWNS

Judith Adams

Senior Authors
Carl B. Smith
Ronald Wardhaugh
Literature Consultant
Rudine Sims

Macmillan Publishing Co., Inc.
New York
Collier Macmillan Publishers
London

D1532112

Copyright © 1975 Macmillan Publishing Co., Inc.

All rights reserved. No part of this book may be reproduced or transmitted in any form or by any means, electronic or mechanical, including photocopying, recording, or by any information storage and retrieval system, without permission in writing from the Publisher.

Macmillan Publishing Co., Inc.
866 Third Avenue, New York, N.Y. 10022
Collier-Macmillan Canada, Ltd.

Printed in the United States of America   10—R
ISBN 0-02-120730-5

Editor: *Kim Choi*

Art direction: *Zlata Paces*

ACKNOWLEDGMENTS

Cover Design: *Norman Gorbaty Design Inc.* Illustrators: Ray Cruz, pp. 4-5; David McPhail, pp. 6-19; Michelle Murdocca, pp. 20-21; Sims Taback, pp. 24-39; Joanne Scribner, pp. 40-51; Philip Wende, pp. 56-73; James Foote, pp. 74-79; Lewis Friedland, pp. 80-81; Richard Brown, pp. 84-93.

The publisher gratefully acknowledges permission to reprint the following copyrighted material:

"Joe the Bear and Sam the Mouse" from *How Joe the Bear and Sam the Mouse Got Together* by Beatrice Schenk de Regniers. Copyright © 1965 by Beatrice Schenk de Regniers. Reprinted by permission of Parents' Magazine Press.

"Ice Cream" by Lynn Mead from *City Streets,* compiled by Lee Bennett Hopkins. Copyright © 1970. Reprinted by permission of Alfred A. Knopf, Inc.

"If I were a sandwich . . ." from *The Rose on My Cake* by Karla Kuskin. Copyright © 1964 by Karla Kuskin. Reprinted by permission of Harper & Row, Publishers, Inc.

"Things That Go Together" from *Just Think!* by Betty Miles and Joan Blos. Copyright © 1971 by Betty Miles. Reprinted by permission of Alfred A. Knopf, Inc.

"Silly Sam" from *Silly Sam* by Leonore Klein. Copyright © 1969 by Scholastic Magazines, Inc. Adapted and reprinted by permission of Scholastic Magazines, Inc.

"Look" from *All That Sunlight* by Charlotte Zolotow. Copyright © 1967 by Charlotte Zolotow. Reprinted by permission of Harper & Row, Publishers, Inc.

"The Donkey Knows" adapted from "I Think I Know" from *Fried Onions and Marshmallows and Other Little Plays for Little People* by Sally Melcher Jarvis. Reprinted by permission of Parents' Magazine Press.

Ups and Downs

CONTENTS

Beatrice Schenk de Regniers

I like to live in a **big** house.

I like to live in a little house.

Then we can't live together.
Boo-hoo.   Boo-hoo.

What Do You Like to Do?

Do you like to play ball?

Yes, I love to play ball.

Then we can play ball together!

Then we can't play ball together.
Boo-hoo. Boo-hoo.

Do you like to ride a bike?

Yes, I love to ride a bike.

Then we can ride a bike together!

I like to ride s-l-o-w.

I like to ride fast.

13

Then we can't ride a bike together.

Good-by, Sam.

Boo-hoo.
Good-by, Joe.
Good-by.

Let's Be Friends

It is three o'clock.
I am going to eat ice cream.
Every day at three o'clock
I eat ice cream.

I am going to eat ice cream, too.
Every day at three o'clock
I eat ice cream.

16

17

What kind of ice cream
do you eat, Sam?

All kinds of ice cream.
What kind of ice cream
do **you** eat, Joe?

I eat all kinds of ice cream, too!

Then we can eat ice cream together.

You will live in a **big** house.
I will live in a little house.
You will play football
and ride s-l-o-w.
I will play baseball
and ride fast.

But every day
at three o'clock...
Yes, every day
at three o'clock...

...we will eat ice cream
together!

Ice Cream

Ice cream
Is cold, soft, sweet
So delightful and cool.
It comes in good flavors, too. But...
It drips!

—Lynn Mead

21

Long and Short Names

My name is Patricia.
Call me Pat.

My name is
Michael.
Call me Mike.

Do you have a
short name?

Cat?

My name is
Caterpillar.
Call me Cat.

22

My name is
Jennifer.
Call me Jenny.

My name is
Thomas.
Call me
Tom.

My name is
James.
Call me Jim.

My name
is Katherine.
Call me
Kathy.

My name is
Hippopotamus.
Call me Hippo.

23

A SURPRISE FOR GRANDMA

Lenore Israel

"We will be gone
for two days,"
said Mother.
"Grandma will
take care of you girls.
And she will
take care of the house."

"What can we do?"
asked Minna and Myra.

"You can be good girls," said Father.
"And you can have fun.
You can play and ride your bikes.
Grandma will take care of things."

The family said good-by.
Then Mother and Father were gone.

Grandma said to the girls,
"I like fun, too!
Minna, you take your red bike.
Myra, you take your green bike.
And I'll take the old bike
with no paint on it.
Let's ride to the woods."

26

In the woods Grandma said,
"I have a ball with me.
Let's play and have fun."

The two girls played ball in the woods
with Grandma.

"Grandma likes to play ball,"
said Minna.

"And it is fun to play with her,"
said Myra.

Then Grandma said,
"It looks like rain."

"I love to run in the rain,"
said Minna.

"So do I," said Myra.

"Me, too," said Grandma.
"Let's run!"

The Girls Take Care of Things

In the morning Grandma said,
"I have a cold this morning.
You girls go out and have fun.
I will sit in the house.
That will help my cold."

Minna and Myra were going out to play.
But Minna said,
"Grandma wants to take care
of her cold.
Who will take care of things
in the house?"

Then Minna looked at Myra.
And Myra looked at Minna.

"We will," said the girls.

"What can we do to help?" asked Myra.

"Grandma will want to eat lunch,"
said Minna.
"So we can be the cooks this morning!
Come on.
I'll find a pot to cook lunch in."

"And I'll find things to cook,"
said Myra.

31

"Look!
I found a fish," said Myra.
"And here are two eggs."

"Fish and eggs go into the pot,"
said Minna.

"And here is a can of soup,"
said Myra.

"Soup into the pot!" said Minna.

"Fish and eggs and soup," said Minna.
"Let's find one other thing to cook."

Myra looked and looked.
And then she said,
"I know!
Ice cream!
I love ice cream."

"Ice cream into the pot!" said Minna.

"Fish and eggs and soup for lunch,"
said Minna.

"And ice cream!" said Myra.
"What a surprise for Grandma!"

Grandma looked at her lunch,
and she laughed.
"This is a surprise!" she said.

Mother and Father Come Home

Minna, Myra, and Grandma were playing ball again when a car drove up.

"Mother!
Father!"

"I didn't think you liked to play ball,"
said Father to Grandma.

"But I do," said Grandma.
"And I love playing with the girls.
But Minna and Myra were
a big help to me, too.
Tell what you did today, girls."

"Grandma wanted to take care
of her cold today," said Minna.
"So Myra and I gave her lunch.
I think Grandma liked her lunch.
When she saw it,
she laughed and laughed."

"What did you cook for Grandma?"
asked Mother.

"We cooked something good,"
said Myra.
"When you have a cold,
we will cook something good for you."

"I think I'll like that," said Mother.

Grandma and the girls laughed.

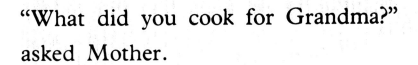

37

If I Were a Sandwich

If I were a sandwich,
I'd sit on a plate
And think of my middle
Until someone ate
Me.
End of the sandwich.

—Karla Kuskin

39

John's Bad Morning

Norah Smaridge

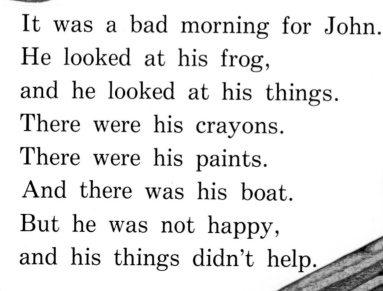

It was a bad morning for John.
He looked at his frog,
and he looked at his things.
There were his crayons.
There were his paints.
And there was his boat.
But he was not happy,
and his things didn't help.

40

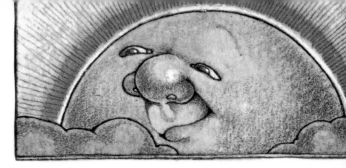

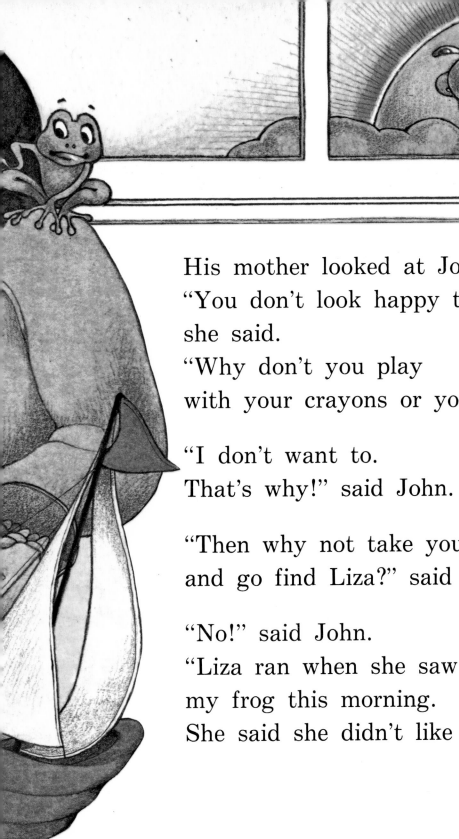

His mother looked at John.
"You don't look happy to me,"
she said.
"Why don't you play
with your crayons or your paints?"

"I don't want to.
That's why!" said John.

"Then why not take your frog
and go find Liza?" said his mother.

"No!" said John.
"Liza ran when she saw
my frog this morning.
She said she didn't like it."

"This **is** a bad morning for you,"
said his mother.
"Why don't you..."

But John didn't wait.
He ran out of the house
with his things.
And then—
he threw his boat
into the garbage can!

Liza was there,
and she saw what John did.

"Don't do that, John!
I love that red boat!" said Liza.

"I can do what I like
with my things," said John.
"**Look.**"

He threw his paints
into the garbage can.
He threw his crayons in, too.
Then he laughed.

"That's not funny, John!" she said.

"I think it is," said John.
"Go home, Liza,
or **you** will go
into the garbage can, too."

Liza wanted to play with John.
But she saw it was a bad morning.
So she went home.
And John ran to the park.

44

John's Afternoon

John ran into the park.
He thought of the morning.
He thought of the things
he threw out.
He thought of Liza.

He saw two little boys
with a big box.

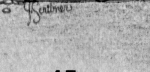

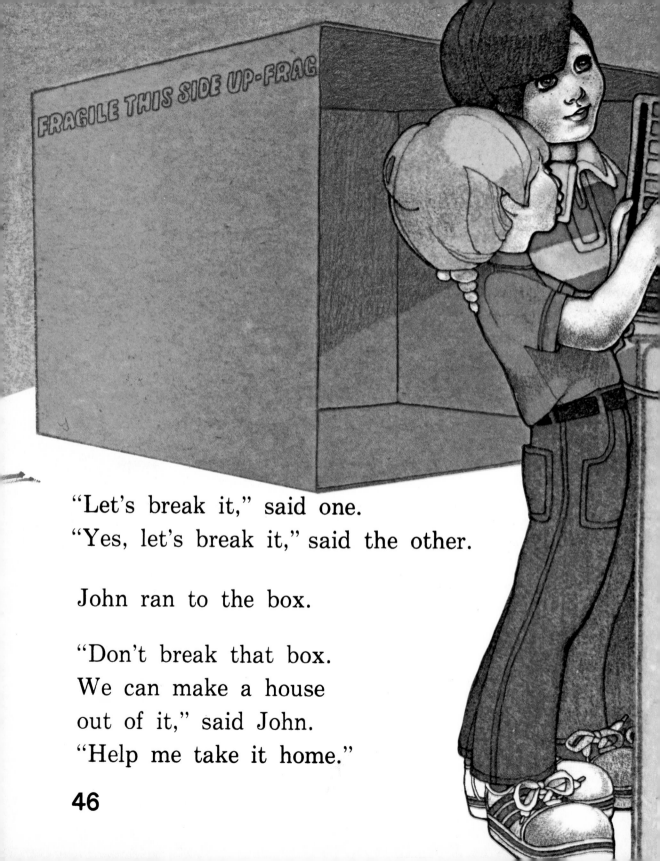

"Let's break it," said one.
"Yes, let's break it," said the other.

John ran to the box.

"Don't break that box.
We can make a house
out of it," said John.
"Help me take it home."

46

John went home with the boys
and the box.

In the afternoon John looked
in the garbage can.
There were his paints
and his crayons.

"I'll paint the house," John said.
"And you can make windows."

"Let's make big windows,"
said the two little boys.

Mother saw the house.

"I love the windows!" she said.
"I'll make you a doorway.
Then you can go in."

When there was a doorway,
the boys went into the box.
And so did John's frog.

Then a girl looked in
at the doorway.
It was Liza.

"You can't come in," said John.
"My frog is in here with me.
And you don't like it."

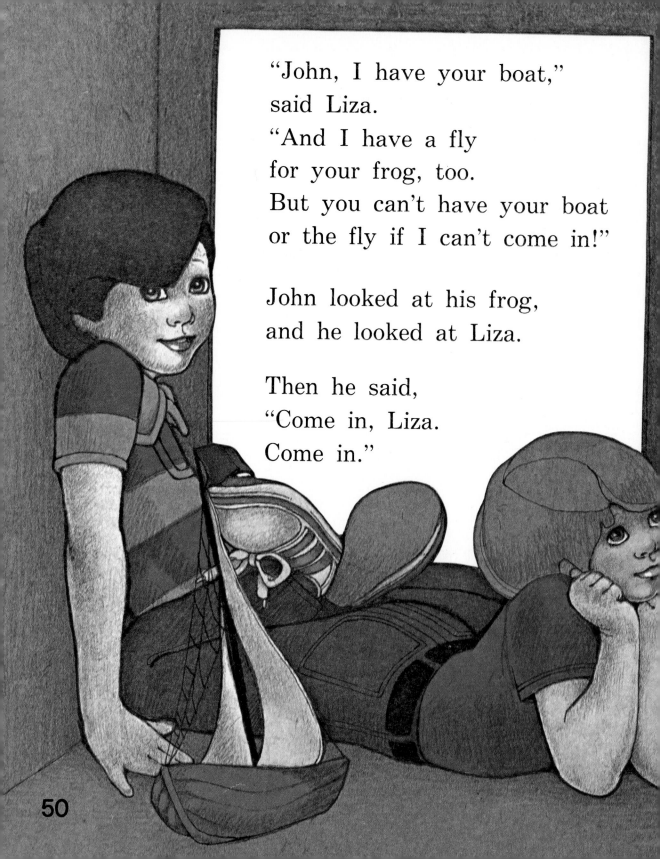

"John, I have your boat,"
said Liza.
"And I have a fly
for your frog, too.
But you can't have your boat
or the fly if I can't come in!"

John looked at his frog,
and he looked at Liza.

Then he said,
"Come in, Liza.
Come in."

It was a bad morning.
But it was a good afternoon.

52

Things That Go Together

Thunder and lightning go together.
So do hands and mittens,

Beans and rice, fire and ice,
Mother cats and kittens.

News and weather go together.
So do reading and writing,
Fish and bones!
Ice cream and cones!
Also, loving and fighting.

Betty Miles and Joan Blos

Go-Togethers

Mouse goes
with cat

and coat goes
with hat.

and
boys and
girls go
with ball.

Telephone goes
with call

Now you think of some.

Windows go with ....

Boat goes with ....

Crayons go with ....

Frog goes with ....

Boo-hoo goes with ....

Eggs go with ....

Grandma goes with ....

Bikes go with ....

SILLY SAM

Leonore Klein

Silly Sam was going to a party.

It was a party for Alice.

He put on his shoes.

He put on his hat.

He put on his coat.

And he went to the party.

Silly Sam went by a man
with a fish.

"I am going to a party for Alice,"
said Silly Sam.
"Do you know what present
I can give her?
She has books and hats
and balls and crayons.
She has all kinds of things
to play with.
What present can I give her?"

"Does she have a fish
that can jump up and down?"
asked the man.

"No," said Silly Sam.

"I will give you a fish
that can jump up and down,"
said the man.
"Stop by a lake and put in the fish.
He will jump up and down.
But you have to give me your shoes."

Silly Sam wanted a present
for Alice.
So he gave the man his shoes.

Silly Sam went by a lake.

"I will stop and put in the fish,"
said Silly Sam.
"I want to see it jump
up and down."

Silly Sam put in the fish.

"Jump!" he said.

But the fish did not jump.
Sam looked, and the fish was gone.
"Stop!" called Silly Sam.
But the fish did not stop.

"What will I do?"
said Silly Sam.
"Alice has all kinds of things
to play with.
I have no present for her.
And I have no shoes."

The Fly That Was Not There

Silly Sam went on his way.
He saw a boy with a box.

"I will stop and ask this boy
if he can help me," said Silly Sam.

"I am on my way to a party for Alice,"
said Silly Sam.
"Do you know what present
I can give her?
She has books and hats
and balls and crayons.
She has all kinds of things
to play with."

"Does she have a fly
that no one can see?"
asked the boy.

"No," said Silly Sam.

"I will give you a fly
that no one can see," said the boy.
"But you have to give me your hat."

Silly Sam wanted a present
for Alice.
So he gave the boy his hat.

Silly Sam wanted to see the fly.
So he looked in the box.
But he didn't see a fly.
He looked and looked.
But there was no fly in the box.

"What will I do?" said Silly Sam.
"I have no present for Alice.
I have no shoes, and I have no hat."

Silly Sam went on his way.

Good-by, Bird

Silly Sam saw a little girl
with a gold cage.
There was a gold bird in the cage.

"I am on my way to a party
for Alice," said Silly Sam.
"Do you know what present
I can give her?
She has books and hats
and balls and crayons.
She has all kinds of things
to play with."

"Does she have a bird
that can fly very high?"
asked the little girl.

"No," said Silly Sam.

"I will give you a bird
that can fly very high.
But you have to give me your coat."

Silly Sam wanted a present
for Alice.
So he gave the girl his coat.

Silly Sam wanted to see
the bird fly very high.
So he looked in the gold cage.
And the bird flew out.
It flew up high.
It flew up very high.
Then it flew away.

"What will I do?" said Silly Sam.

"I have no present for Alice.

The fish did not jump up and down.

There was no fly in the box.

The bird flew away.

And I gave away my shoes, my hat,
and my coat."

At the Party

Silly Sam was very sad.
He looked back at the cage.
Then he looked back
at the cage again.
And he saw a little gold egg.

"I will go to the party,"
said Silly Sam.
"And I will give Alice this egg.
I have no other present for her."

The girls and the boys at the party
laughed at Silly Sam.
There he was
without shoes,
without a hat,
and without a coat on his back.
And the boys and girls laughed
at his little present, too.

But Alice looked at the egg.
And, as she looked, it cracked.
And then it cracked a little more.
And then it cracked a little more.

There, in the egg,
was a little gold bird.
It was a little gold bird
for Alice.

"A gold bird!" said Alice.
"I love my present, Sam.
I do!"

Silly Sam had no shoes.
He had no hat.
And he had no coat.
But he didn't care.
He had a happy friend.

Rosa and Her Shadow

Judith Adams

When Rosa goes out to play,

she is not alone.

Her shadow is there.

She can't go out without it.

Or can she?

She puts on her hat and goes out.

Rosa is quiet, very quiet.

She thinks she is alone.

Then she slowly looks back.

And what does she see?

Her shadow!

She was so quiet, too.

Rosa takes her time as she walks.
And her shadow takes its time, too.
Then she sees her friends
and she runs.
And her shadow runs
to be there with her.

When Rosa goes home to eat,
she is not alone.
Her shadow is there all the time.

What if Rosa wants to be alone?
She can't put her shadow in a box.
And she can't give it away.
How **do** you say good-by to a shadow?

DO YOU KNOW?

Look

Firelight and shadows
dancing on the wall.
Look at my shadow
TEN FEET TALL!

— Charlotte Zolotow

Word Magic

Be a word magician.
Change a letter and
make a new word.

Turn f<u>u</u>n into f_n

b<u>a</u>d into b_d

an<u>d</u> into an_

<u>l</u>ake into _ake

ma<u>n</u> into ma_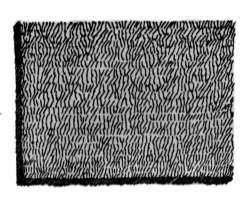

h<u>a</u>t into h_t

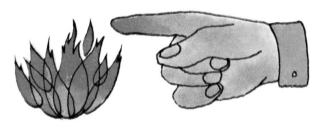

<u>p</u>ark into _ark

<u>t</u>ell into _ell

b<u>i</u>g into b_g

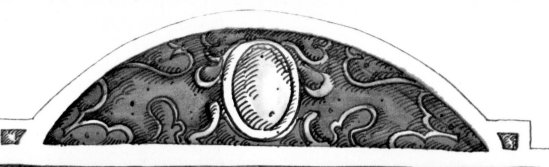

The Donkey Knows

IN THIS PLAY

Donkey

Donkey Man

Walking Man

Sally Melcher Jarvis

TIME: Day

PLACE: Country road
(*Walking Man is walking
down the road.
Donkey Man rides down
the road on his donkey.*)

Walking Man: This is a hot day.
It is too hot to walk.
(*He sees Donkey Man
on his donkey.*)
Will you give me a ride?
I will give you money.

85

Donkey Man: Yes!
Give me your money.

Walking Man: Here you are.
*(He gives Donkey Man money,
and he jumps on Donkey.)*

86

Donkey Man: How hot it is!
I think I will stop for water.

Donkey: *(to himself)*
Will they think of me?
(Walking Man and Donkey Man
stop for water.
They don't give water to Donkey.)

Walking Man: I think I will sit down.

Donkey: *(to himself)*
Can't I sit down, too?

Walking Man: It is so hot!
I think I will sit
in the shadow of the donkey!

Donkey Man: No, you don't!
There is a place for one man here.
It is **my** donkey.
I think I will sit in his shadow.

Walking Man: I gave you money.
I will sit there!
*(He sits down in the shadow
of Donkey.)*

Donkey: *(to himself)*
I am hot,
but they didn't give me water.

Donkey Man: You gave me money
to ride my donkey.
You didn't give me money
to sit in his shadow.
I will sit there!
*(He pushes Walking Man
out of the shadow.)*

Walking Man: Don't do that!
(*He pushes Donkey Man,
and he pushes Donkey.*)

Donkey: *(to himself)*
I think I will run away!
(*He runs away.*)

Donkey Man: Come back! Come back!

Walking Man: He is gone!

Donkey Man: It is so hot.
And we have to walk.
There is no shadow for you
or for me.

Walking Man: Why do you think the donkey
ran away?

Donkey Man: I don't know.

Walking Man: And **I** don't know.

92

Donkey: *(He is down the road.
He looks back.)*
I know why!

93

WORD LIST

The new words introduced in this book are listed below beside the page number on which they first appear. The children should be able to independently identify italicized words at this level.

6. Joe	18. kind	31. *lunch*
7. Sam	all	cooks
9. am	*kinds*	pot
looking	24. Grandma	*cook*
together	*days*	32. eggs
10. boo-hoo	take	soup
11. play	care	35. *playing*
ball	*asked*	when
love	Minna	36. think
12. football	Myra	today
baseball	25. *good*	37. *cooked*
13. bike	fun	*something*
slow	*bikes*	40. John's
14. good-by	27. *played*	bad
16. o'clock	29. morning	*John*
eat	cold	frog
ice		crayons
cream		boat
every		41. Liza

42. threw
    garbage
45. afternoon
    thought
46. break
    make
47. windows
48. doorway
56. silly
    Alice
    put
    shoes
    coat
57. by
    give
    has
    balls
58. stop
61. *called*

62. *way*
66. gold
    cage
67. very
68. flew
    away
70. back
    egg
71. *without*
72. cracked
    more
73. had
74. Rosa
    shadow
    goes
    alone
    puts
    quiet
    thinks

76. *takes*
    time
    its
78. how
84. donkey
    knows
    walking
85. road
    hot
    money
86. gives
87. water
    himself
    they
90. pushes